A MESSAGE TO PARENTS & TEACHERS:

In this new series of inexpensive books for children, Rand McNally is presenting carefully selected, good literature for the very young child. Books in this series are factual, fanciful, humorous, questioning and adventurous. It is hoped that the series will provide for the masses of children whose parents might be unaware of the availability of good literature at such nominal cost. We firmly believe that the love and appreciation of literature must begin when the child is very young.

If one takes the time to absorb the interests and wonders of the city, there is much to do and much to see. The city holds a world of learning and pleasure on trips to the parks, the zoo and museums, or in watching its workers. The activities suggested in this book are free or inexpensive.

We hope that adults will put aside their preoccupations as they accompany children and with them, feel and share the movement, interests and excitement that the city offers in its everyday life.

NATIONAL COLLEGE OF EDUCATION
Evanston, Illinois

ALL AROUND
THE CITY

By Diane Sherman

Illustrated by Manning de V. Lee

RAND McNALLY & COMPANY · Chicago

Established 1856

Hurrah for the city!
What fun it can be!
There's so much to do,
And so much to see,

The park is a grand place.
You sit on a seat
And sprinkle some peanuts
For pigeons to eat.

Next to the benches
Are seesaws and slides,
And a smooth little pathway
For bicycle rides.

Listen, there's music!
We're lucky today!
The band's on the platform.
They're starting to play.

Where shall we go,
Now the concert is done?
We *could* take a bus ride.
Does that sound like fun?

Or, the museum's
A good place to go
To see dinosaurs
That lived long ago.

Only *real* animals
Live in the Zoo.
Come see the monkeys!
They're clowning for you!

Time to head home now.
Just walking's a treat,
So much is happening
Here on the street!

See the construction crew
Working up high,
Walking on girders,
While we pass by.

Other men drill
In the street down below,
Making a place
For the new pipes to go.

Hear that loud wailing!
It's sirens! They say,
"Fire engines coming!
Get out of the way!"

Policemen blow whistles!
Traffic lights flash.
Crowds hustle by you,
While trucks collect trash.

Men unload boxes,
And look! Over there,
Workers wash windows
Way up in the air.

Sometimes, perhaps,
You can stay up at night
To see the whole city
Sparkling with light,